GRADE
5

The 2007 & 2008 Syllabus shou[ld] requirements, especially those sight-reading. Attention should be p[aid] Notices, where warning is given of any changes.

The syllabus is obtainable online at www.abrsm.org, from music retailers or from the Services Department, The Associated Board of the Royal Schools of Music, 24 Portland Place, London W1B 1LU, United Kingdom (please send a stamped addressed C5 (162mm x 229mm) envelope).

In exam centres outside the UK, information and syllabuses may be obtained from the Local Representative.

CONTENTS

Where appropriate, pieces in this volume have been checked with original source material and edited as necessary for instructional purposes. Any editorial additions to the texts are given in small print, within square brackets, or – in the case of slurs and ties – in the form ⌢ . Fingering, phrasing, pedalling, metronome marks and the editorial realization of ornaments (where given) are for guidance only; they are not comprehensive or obligatory.

Editor for the Associated Board: **Richard Jones**

DO NOT
PHOTOCOPY
© MUSIC

Alternative pieces for this grade

Music origination by Barnes Music Engraving Ltd
Cover by Økvik Design
Printed in England by Headley Brothers Ltd,
The Invicta Press, Ashford, Kent

Andante in B flat

K. 15ii

MOZART

This piece is drawn from the so-called 'London Notebook', a collection of keyboard pieces composed by Mozart at the ages of eight and nine during the Mozart family's visit to England in 1764–5. All slurs and dynamics are editorial suggestions only. The source is quite erroneous, and a few corrections have been made by the editor.

Source: autograph MS, Biblioteka Jagiellońska, Kraków

Sonata in A

Kp. 74

D. SCARLATTI

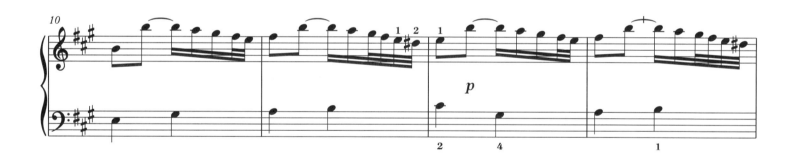

Domenico Scarlatti (1685–1757) was a son of the celebrated opera composer Alessandro. Born in Naples, he settled first in Portugal and later in Spain, where he cultivated a boldly original style of writing for the keyboard. The Sonata in A, Kp. 74, is one of his earlier pieces, apparently predating his famous published collection, the *Essercizi* (30 sonatas) of 1738. All slurs and dynamics are editorial suggestions only.
Source: Venice XIV (1742), No. 38

Scherzo in A

No. 45 from *Anweisung zum Piano-forte Spiel*

Edited by
Timothy Roberts

J. N. HUMMEL

Johann Nepomuk Hummel (1778–1837) was an Austrian contemporary of Beethoven. A child prodigy, and one of Mozart's pupils, he later became famous throughout Europe as a virtuoso pianist. The Scherzo in A is drawn from his massive piano method, the *Anweisung zum Piano-forte Spiel* (Instruction in Playing the Pianoforte), which was published in 1828.
Source: *Ausführlich theoretisch-practische Anweisung zum Piano-forte Spiel* (Vienna: T. Haslinger, 1828)

La chevaleresque

No. 25 from *25 études faciles et progressives*, Op. 100

B:1

J. F. F. BURGMÜLLER

The German composer Johann Friedrich Franz Burgmüller (1806–74) settled in Paris after 1832 and became a popular pianist, improvising hundreds of salon pieces and composing a great many instructional works. The title of this piece translates as 'The Knight Errant'. In the exam the repeats should not be played.

Source: *25 études faciles et progressives*, Op. 100 (London, 1854)

B:2

Gigue

No. 9 from *Zehn kleine Vortragsstücke*, Op. 44

REGER

linke Hand oben
[left hand above]

rechte Hand oben
[right hand above]
una corda

Max Reger (1873–1916) was a German composer who studied with Hugo Riemann in Wiesbaden, and later became director of music at Leipzig University and director of the court orchestra at Meiningen. He was an extremely prolific composer, especially of piano and organ works, songs and chamber music. The *Zehn kleine Vortragsstücke* (Ten Small Performance Pieces), from which this Gigue is drawn, were composed in 1900. In this piece, the editor has altered the position of some of the dynamics for clarity.

Source: *Zehn kleine Vortragsstücke für Pianoforte zum Gebrauche beim Unterricht*, Op. 44 (Leipzig: J. Aibl, 1900)

Adapted from *A Keyboard Anthology*, Second Series, Book 3, edited by Howard Ferguson (ABRSM Publishing)

tre corde

B:3

Romance

No. 10 from *Zehn Fantasiestücke*, Op. 17

REINECKE

Carl Reinecke (1824–1910) was for many years conductor of the celebrated Leipzig Gewandhaus Orchestra and professor of piano and composition at the Leipzig Conservatory, where his pupils included Grieg and Sullivan. His huge output includes many piano pieces in the style of Schumann.

Source: *Zehn Fantasiestücke*, Op. 17 (London: Augener, 1880)

© 2006 by The Associated Board of the Royal Schools of Music

Jackson Street Blues

from *Jazz, Rags & Blues*, Book 4

MARTHA MIER

Martha Mier is a piano teacher, composer and adjudicator in Lake City, Florida. She specializes in writing educational piano music and is especially known for her popular series *Jazz, Rags & Blues* and *Romantic Impressions*.

Burlesque

No. 36 from *Kleine Klavierstücke*, Op. 37

WINDSPERGER

Lothar Windsperger (1885–1935) was a German composer who studied at the Munich Academy of Music, taught theory and piano at Wiesbaden, and was later appointed director of the Mainz Music School. From 1913 he worked as an editor and adviser with the publishing company Schott of Mainz.

Source: *Kleine Klavierstücke*, Op. 37 (Mainz & Leipzig, 1927)

Fanfare

from *Vignettes*, Op. 43a

DEJAN DESPIĆ

Dejan Despić (b. 1930) is a Serbian composer who studied at the Belgrade Academy of Music and, from 1965 to 1995, taught at Belgrade University of the Arts. His music is written in a neo-classical style. A suitable tempo for this piece in the exam would be ♩. = c.104.

© 1966 by Musikverlage Hans Gerig, Köln

© 1980 assigned to Breitkopf & Härtel, Wiesbaden. All enquiries for this piece apart from the exams should be addressed to Breitkopf & Härtel, Walkmühlstraße 52, 65195 Wiesbaden, Germany.